D1317095

THE OFFICIAL BOOK OF

ME

■ SCHOLASTIC

Written by Heather Dakota

Illustrated & Designed
by Nancy Panaccione

All rights reserved. No part of this publication
may be reproduced, or stored in a retrieval
system, or transmitted in any form or by any
means, electronic, mechanical, photocopying,
recording, or otherwise, without written
permission of Tangerine Press.

Copyright © 2013 Scholastic Inc.

an imprint of
SCHOLASTIC
www.scholastic.com

Scholastic and Tangerine Press and associated
logos are trademarks of Scholastic Inc.

Published by Tangerine Press,
an imprint of Scholastic Inc.,
557 Broadway; New York, NY 10012

10 9 8 7 6 5 4 3 2 1

ISBN: 978-0-545-57727-4

Printed and bound in Shenzhen, China

This IS THE OFFICIAL BOOK OF THE awesome ME

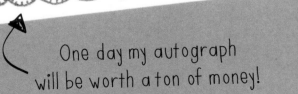

One day my autograph will be worth a ton of money!

Details ♡

Full name: Anna Doris Demeo
My nickname: Monkey, munchain
My name means: strong
My birthday: January 6th Birthstone: Garnet

The name I would have chosen
(besides the one I have): Marlie

My age:
(circle number)

5 6 7 8 ⑨ 10
11 12 13 14 15
16 17 18

Distinguishing features
(Birthmarks and beauty marks):
freckles.

I wish I were:
(circle number)

⑬ 14 15 16 17
18 19 20 21

My astrological sign:

My eye color:

The gorgeous and talented me.

(Tape, draw, or glue a picture of you on this page.)

My best features:

HERE I AM!

My hair is:
- curly
- straight
- wavy
- blonde
- brown
- red
- black

Words I live by
(my motto):

THE INSIDE SCOOP

MY FATHER'S FAMILY WAS FROM:

MY MOTHER'S FAMILY WAS FROM:

I'm so **happy** when:

I get **anxious** when:

I **have to have:**

3 little words that describe me:

OOPS!
My bad habits:

I'm hopeful about:

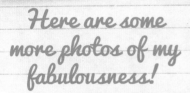

Here are some more photos of my fabulousness!

Paste or draw pictures of you and your friends, your pets, your family, and what you love to do...right here!

LOOKIN' GOOD

My Kinda Day

This song is my jam:

I just talked to:

We talked about:

_____
_____
_____
_____
_____

Right now I'm thinking a lot **about:**

MY **favorite food** I ATE TODAY:

MY **favorite drink** OF THE DAY:

A FABULOUS **smell** I SMELLED TODAY:

I WAS **happy** TODAY WHEN:

THE **most fun thing** I DID TODAY:

What I'm wearing right now:

But I really wanted to wear:

When I go to sleep: ___ : ___ am / pm

When I really want to go to sleep: ___ : ___ am / pm

Everything I LOVE about me.

Write down, doodle, or scribble all the things that you LOVE about yourself! No holding back!

Those *Sweet* Smells Quiz

1. After school, you're:
A. Picking flowers in your garden.
B. Playing sports.
C. Studying.
D. Going to the mall.

2. Your friends describe you as:
A. Romantic and passionate.
B. Energetic and active.
C. Laid-back and easygoing.
D. Practical and realistic.

3. Favorite exercise:
A. Yoga
B. Kick-boxing
C. Hiking
D. Dancing

4. The celeb whose style you love:
A. Taylor Swift: fresh and sweet
B. Rihanna: spicy and hot
C. Selena Gomez: flirty and girlie
D. Kristen Stewart: mysterious and quiet

5. You go crazy for the smell of:
A. Fresh roses.
B. Homemade cookies.
C. Sheets hung on the line to dry.
D. Orange, lime, or grapefruit.

6. If your life were a movie, it would be:
A. A romance
B. An action adventure
C. A comedy
D. A drama

7. The best compliment someone could give you is:
A. "You're so sweet!"
B. "You're so adventurous!"
C. "You're easy-going!"
D. "You're so funny!"

8. Your favorite foods are:
A. Dessert!
B. Tacos and chicken wings.
C. A yummy salad!
D. Anything you can make in under 15 minutes.

9. Your favorite actor is:
A. Robert Pattinson. Cute and funny!
B. Taylor Lautner. Hot, hot, hot!
C. Chris Hemsworth. Real men are superheroes!
D. Johnny Depp. 'Nuff said!

Add it up:

	A	B	C	D
1.				
2.				
3.				
4.				
5.				
6.				
7.				
8.				
9.				
10.				
totals:				

10. Your makeup must-haves are:

A. *Lip gloss and blush. Shiny lips and rosy cheeks are so sweet.*

B. *Eye shadow, liner, and mascara. Beguiling eyes are a must!*

C. *Sunscreen — you're outside so much, you have to.*

D. *Lip balm — easy-peasy!*

How'd You Do? Results

Mostly A's? Your special scent is Floral!
You're sensual and emotional, so florals are best for you.
They'll make you feel like you're in your own garden!

Mostly B's? Your special scent is Spicy!
Warm, spicy fragrances spark your adventurous and
passionate personality, making you feel hot, hot, hot!

Mostly C's? Your special scent is Natural!
You're so nurturing and earthy, light scents or no scents
will work best for you.

Mostly D's? Your special scent is Super Fresh!
You're a "go, go, go" girl! Lively, citrusy scents will keep up
with your fun-loving personality.

MY FAMILY UNIT

My Parentals are:
- ○ married
- ○ divorced
- ○ separated
- ○ never married

My **favorite** relative is:

My grandparents live:
- ○ close by   ○ in the same state, but not the same town
- ○ out of state   ○ out of the country   ○ on the road

i look like:
- ○ My mom
- ○ My dad

i have _____ siblings.
Three words that describe our relationship:

1 ....

2 ....

3 ....

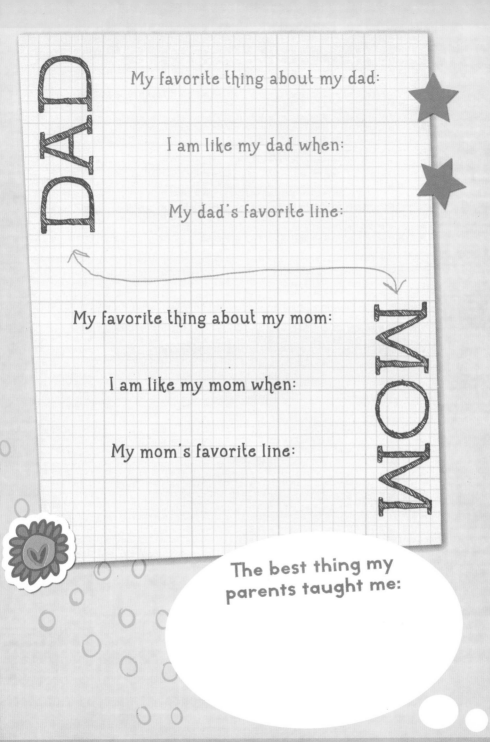

DAD

My favorite thing about my dad:

I am like my dad when:

My dad's favorite line:

My favorite thing about my mom:

I am like my mom when:

My mom's favorite line:

MOM

The best thing my parents taught me:

Dear Mom and Dad,

Love,

Family Tree

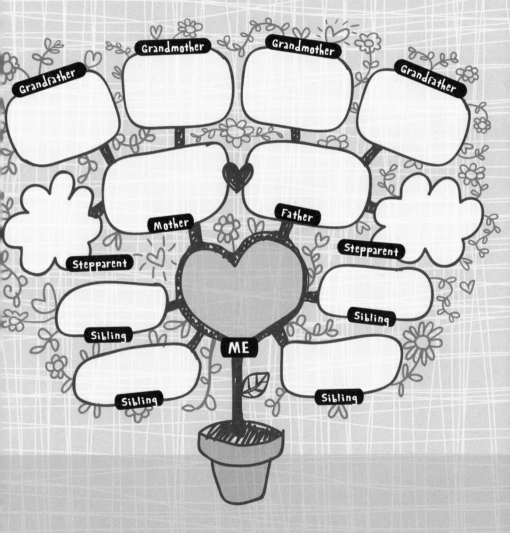

The Younger Me

i was born:

I am the:
★ only ★ youngest
★ middle ★ oldest
child.

My **favorite** food was:

I spent my summers:

When I was little, the **best hiding place** was:

One thing i would change about my childhood:

My favorite stuffed animal was:

My favorite toy was:

The kid thing **i still love** today is:

My best **childhood friend** was:

My **imaginary friend** was:

My **secret hideout** was:

My favorite games **were:**

My favorite cartoons **were:**

My favorite kiddie movie was:

The movie I watched but wasn't supposed to was:

I was just a kid then.

My best memory of being a kid is when...

My Childhood
Memory Album

Tape or glue photos from your childhood on these pages.
You can make photocopies of photos. Or use images you
find in magazines that remind you of your younger
years. Don't forget to add some funny captions.

Home Sweet Home

I live in:

_____
City

_____
State

I like to go to

_____
friend's name

house, because:

_____

_____

_____

My favorite thing to **do at home** is:

My **favorite smell** in the house is:

My house is **awesome** because:

The **craziest thing** that ever happened at my house:

My dad cooks the best:

My mom cooks the best:

I can find my favorite snack:
- in the pantry
- in the fridge
- on the kitchen counter
- hidden in my room

The house rule that I can't stand is:

I'm supposed to be home by:

am
pm

MY ✦DREAM✦ HOUSE

Check off all of the things you want for your dream

- ☐ In the mountains _____
  _____
- ☐ In the middle of nowhere _____
  _____
- ☐ In the city _____
  _____
- ☐ In a small town _____
  _____
- ☐ In the country _____
  _____
- ☐ by a beach _____
  _____
- ☐ by a lake _____
  _____
- ☐ In another country _____
  _____
- ☐ Private island _____
  _____
- ☐ Other _____

dream house- details

Basic Description:

- ☐ Small
- ☐ Large
- ☐ Mansion
- ☐ Apartment
- ☐ Old barn
- ☐ Farm
- ☐ Cabin
- ☐ Cottage
- ☐ Loft
- ☐ Castle
- ☐ Other _____

Must-Haves

- ☐ _____
- ☐ _____
- ☐ _____
- ☐ _____
- ☐ _____
- ☐ _____
- ☐ _____
- ☐ _____
- ☐ _____
- ☐ _____
- ☐ _____
- ☐

Furnishings:

- ☐ Four-poster bed
- ☐ Antiques
- ☐ Modern furniture
- ☐ Artwork
- ☐ Cozy chairs
- ☐ Candles
- ☐ Leather couch & chairs
- ☐ Large-screen TV
- ☐ Entertainment system
- ☐ Built-in furniture
- ☐ Houseplants
- ☐ Large windows

dream house - details

Features:

- ☐ Large closets
- ☐ Made with recycled material
- ☐ Four-car garage
- ☐ Front porch
- ☐ Back porch
- ☐ Lots of trees
- ☐ Wood floors
- ☐ Large fireplace
- ☐ Whirlpool bathtub
- ☐ Fenced-in yard
- ☐ Big kitchen
- ☐ Security system
- ☐ Two-story
- ☐ One-story
- ☐ Library
- ☐ Tile floors
- ☐ Carpet
- ☐ Natural materials
- ☐ Brick
- ☐ Circular driveway
- ☐ Other _____

Extras:

- ☐ Flower garden
- ☐ Vegetable garden
- ☐ Fruit trees
- ☐ Waterfall
- ☐ Pool
- ☐ Music studio
- ☐ Art studio
- ☐ Hot tub
- ☐ Sports area
- ☐ Game room
- ☐ Theater
- ☐ Wildlife sanctuary
- ☐ Barn
- ☐ Stables

dream house- details

My House!

Doodle, scribble, or paste anything that reminds you of your home life.

My School Life

I go to:

I am in _____ grade.

My favorite subject in school:

My least favorite subject in school:

My favorite teacher is _____.
Tell why:

My least favorite teacher is _____.
Tell why:

Detention time happens: O regularly O rarely O NEVER!

There are cliques at school: O Yes O No

People at school would describe me as:

I get mostly

(circle answer)

A's

A's & B's

B's

C's

B's & C's

C's

C's & D's

D's

F's

I think popularity is:

I Love
School

O Yes or O No

Mode of Transportation to school:

O Bus   O Bike   O Walk

O Parent drives me   O Sibling drives me

O I'd rather fly!

MY Future Career Quiz

What do you want to be when you grow up?

Take the quiz and find out which career would be best for you.

How would you prefer to spend your summer holiday?
- **A** Taking music classes
- **B** Swimming at the pool
- **C** Visiting Paris, New York, or Milan
- **D** Volunteering at the Humane Society
- **E** Space Camp

Where do you want to live?
- **A** In the mountains
- **B** Wherever there is a great sports team
- **C** New York, Milan, or Paris
- **D** Africa
- **E** Silicon Valley

What do you love to do in your free time?
- **A** Play the piano
- **B** Sports all the way
- **C** Upcycle old clothes
- **D** Brushing the horses
- **E** Reading the latest novel

How would you prefer to spend spring break?
- **A** Taking art classes
- **B** Skiing
- **C** Isn't that Fashion Week?
- **D** Volunteering at an animal shelter
- **E** Science camp

What's your favorite hobby?
- **A** Writing poems
- **B** Lifting weights
- **C** Shopping is a hobby, right?
- **D** Taking care of the neighborhood pets
- **E** Playing chess

In your closet, you'll find:

A. Comfy jeans and band T-shirts
B. Uniforms, tennis shoes, and sports equipment
C. The color of the year
D. Comfy shoes and animal prints
E. Anything that's easy to match

Your birthday is coming up. What would be an ideal gift?

A. Some creative supplies
B. A surfboard
C. I saw the hottest shirt...
D. A cute little hamster
E. There is a book I'm dying to read...

Your favorite subject in school is...

A. Music
B. P.E.
C. Home Ec.
D. Biology
E. Chemistry

What is your favorite outing?

A. Art supply store
B. Any sports field
C. Shoe store
D. Horseback riding
E. The library

What is your biggest pet peeve?

A. When you're interrupted in the middle of a project.
B. People not exercising.
C. Wearing sweatpants to school.
D. When an animal is treated poorly.
E. People who never do their homework.

What's your favorite TV show?

A. TV? I'd rather be creating something.
B. Isn't there a game on?
C. *Say Yes to the Dress*
D. *Dog Whisperer*
E. *Mythbusters*

Add up your answers!

A =
B =
C =
D =
E =

Turn the page for your results! ⟶

The Results

If you're a mix of several letters, don't fret! Many careers involve skills from each of the different groups. **You rock!**

If you answered with mostly **A**'s

Creativity is your middle name. You would make a fabulous artist, musician, graphic designer, photographer, jewelry designer, or writer. Be sure to practice, practice, practice!

If you answered with mostly **B**'s

Football, hockey, baseball, swimming, soccer, tennis, skiing, or volleyball...you name the sport and you're probably watching it or participating. You'll make a fantastic professional athlete or you might just manage a sports team or a gym.

If you answered with mostly **C**'s

You are a fashionista! You are headed for a glamorous life in fashion. You could be a fashion designer, makeup artist, model, or fashion buyer for your favorite store.

If you answered with mostly **D**'s

Animals are your world. They should be a huge part of your career. You will make an excellent veterinarian, zoologist, animal researcher, or pet sitter.

If you answered with mostly **E**'s

Smarty-pants. You are one smart cookie! With your love for science and math, you'll make a fantastic researcher, doctor, CSI investigator, engineer, or computer programmer.

School's Out

After school I:

Instruments I play:

On the weekends,
my friends and I:

Instruments I'd
like to play:

Sports I play:

Sports **I want** to play:

Clubs I belong to:

 My favorite thing to do outside of school is:

My Best Buds

My **BFF** is:

Four important qualities of a friend are:

1

2

3

4

The friend I've known the **longest**:

A friend who is **always there** for me:

The friend who I tell all of **my secrets** to:

The friend who gives the **best advice**:

The friend I **miss the most**:

The **craziest thing** my friends and I have done:

The person I wish
I knew better:

Place **photos** of your friends and write their names below.

Lookin' GOOD!

BFB AWARDS

(Best Friend Bestie)

And the winner is...

Write down the names of your friends who are the **best** in each category.

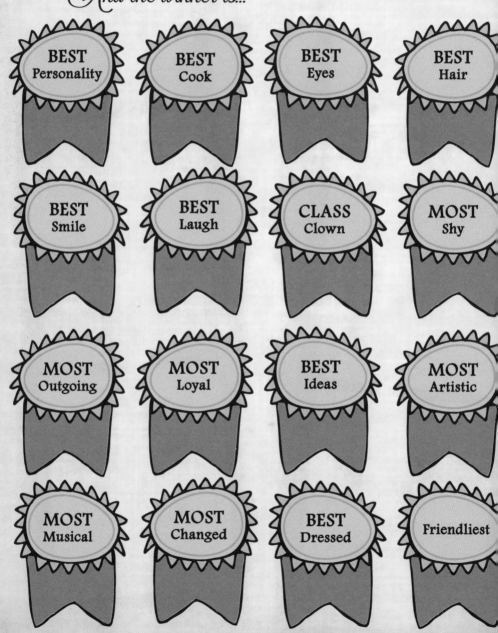

BEST Personality

BEST Cook

BEST Eyes

BEST Hair

BEST Smile

BEST Laugh

CLASS Clown

MOST Shy

MOST Outgoing

MOST Loyal

BEST Ideas

MOST Artistic

MOST Musical

MOST Changed

BEST Dressed

Friendliest

Which of your friends would become...

a comedian

an actor

a writer

an artist

the president

a fashion designer

a pro athlete

a rock star

a vet

a police officer
or firefighter

a singer

a world leader

an architect

a teacher

a world traveler

Socially Speaking

QUIZ

How's your social life? Take this quiz and find out.

Go to the dance with friends.

No! So many friends, so little time.

YOUR SCHOOL IS HAVING A DANCE. YOU WILL:

DO YOU HAVE JUST ONE BFF?

Soccer game, or other sporting event

Yep, the best BFF in the world.

DOES IT TAKE YOU A LONG TIME TO CHOOSE WHAT TO WEAR?

Go with a date.

Start Here

YOUR SATURDAY PLANS

Forever!

Nah, I'm quick to get dressed.

ARE YOU LOW OR HIGH MAINTENANCE?

You have homework and can't make it.

High Maintenance

Stay at home to watch a few movies

Low Maintenance

Takes a while.

YOUR BFF WANTS TO HANG OUT AFTER SCHOOL. YOU TELL HER:

DOES IT TAKE A WHILE FOR YOU TO MAKE FRIENDS, OR DO YOU FIT IN EASILY?

Actually, you would have been the one asking her.

Fit in easily.

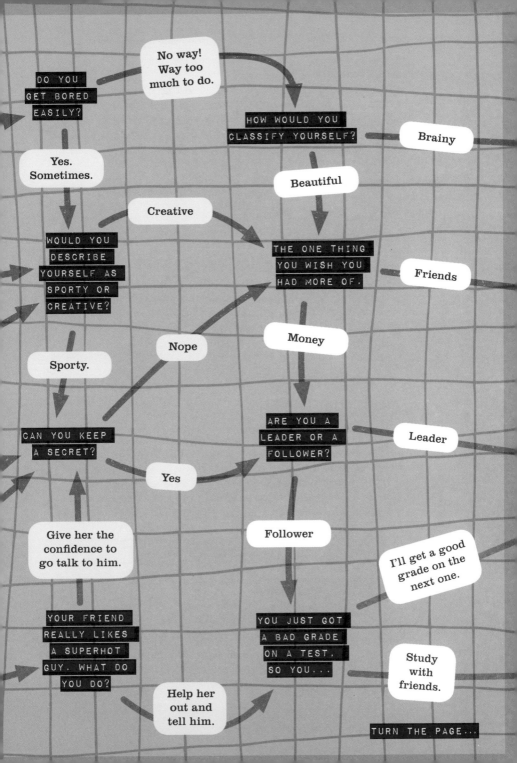

HOME GIRL

You tend to be a quiet, shy person. And that's great! You prefer staying home or going over to your best friend's house for a sleepover rather than partying with a gang of friends. Being supersocial makes you feel a little uncomfortable, but you still know how to have fun. You just prefer it with a few friends. You gain a lot of energy by being alone, too.

SWEETIE PIE

You are full of sugar and grace. You always know what to say and how to act. All you have to do is walk into a room and it lights up. People often call you the peacemaker because you know how to diffuse an argument and talk yourself out of any sticky situation. Everyone adores your sweet personality.

ZANY GAL

There is no one like you! You are a true original, who inspires others to be themselves. You're always doing or thinking about something new. Life is unpredictable and zany...just the way you like it. People know they can't expect consistency from you, but that's okay. You are a great problem solver and are happiest when having fun. No one throws a party like you can.

SOCIAL BUTTERFLY

You are outgoing and friendly. Your friends love being around you. You're confident in social situations, even if you don't know anyone there. People are attracted to your adventurous and daring personality. You're at your best when you're the center of attention. Your take-charge, can-do attitude is what your friends like best about you.

SCRIBBLES & SECRETS

Doodle whatever your social life looks like to you.
The places you go, the things you like to do, and who goes with you. ♥

This can be just words or images, too. Go to town!

I'm Seeing Starz

Paste magazine cutouts of your favorite celebs on these pages.

Emoti-me

- ○ moody **or** ○ calm
- ○ planner **or** ○ spontaneous
- ○ open-minded **or** ○ conservative
- ○ disorganized **or** ○ neat
- ○ anxious **or** ○ laid-back
- ○ shy **or** ○ outgoing
- ○ confident **or** ○ unsure
- ○ drama queen **or** ○ cool
- ○ sweet **or** ○ sour
- ○ adventurous **or** ○ cautious
- ○ free **or** ○ reserved
- ○ generous **or** ○ selfish
- ○ patient **or** ○ impatient
- ○ passive **or** ○ aggressive
- ○ silly **or** ○ serious
- ○ right brain **or** ○ left brain
- ○ logical **or** ○ creative
- ○ black and white **or** ○ colorful
- ○ happy **or** ○ sad
- ○ dark **or** ○ light
- ○ hardworking **or** ○ lazy
- ○ relaxed **or** ○ tense

My Style FILE

Check all that apply to your fashion style.

bottoms
- short shorts
- bermuda shorts
- skirt
- jeans

dresses
- mini-dress
- maxi-dress
- little black dress
- no dress, no way

shoes
- sandals
- flat, but cute
- heels
- tennis shoes

jewelry
- bracelets
- locket necklace
- rings
- earrings

pants
- wide-leg jeans
- leggings
- low-rise jeans
- boyfriend jeans

jackets
- hoodie
- sweater
- fur coat
- school jacket

swimsuits
- bikini
- one-piece
- shorts & a T-shirt
- tank top and wrap

hats
- bandana
- baseball cap
- beret
- knit cap

bags
- fringed hobo bag
- clutch
- backpack
- sac

hair
- headband
- ponytail
- bows
- keep it short

shirts
- T-shirt
- button-up
- silky blouse
- cropped shirt

colors
- black and white
- pink
- all colors
- blue

Say YES to the Dress...

What would you rather wear? Circle YES or NO WAY!

sequins
YES or NO WAY

polka dots
YES or NO WAY

animal prints
YES or NO WAY

big flowers
YES or NO WAY

leather pants
YES or NO WAY

backpack
YES or NO WAY

tutu
YES or NO WAY

cowboy hat
YES or NO WAY

argyle
YES or NO WAY

fur
YES or NO WAY

shiny fabric
YES or NO WAY

socks with sandals
YES or NO WAY

kimono
YES or NO WAY

miniskirt
YES or NO WAY

scarf
YES or NO WAY

poodle skirt
YES or NO WAY

long sleeves
YES or NO WAY

feathers
YES or NO WAY

jeweled shoes
YES or NO WAY

knee-high boots
YES or NO WAY

tie-dye T-shirt
YES or NO WAY

school uniform
YES or NO WAY

high heels
YES or NO WAY

handmade clothes
YES or NO WAY

one-piece bathing suit
YES or NO WAY

a lot of colors
YES or NO WAY

neon colors
YES or NO WAY

black and white only
YES or NO WAY

leggings
YES or NO WAY

stripes with dots
YES or NO WAY

bikini
YES or NO WAY

giant sunglasses
YES or NO WAY

clashing colors
YES or NO WAY

Christmas sweater
YES or NO WAY

floppy hat
YES or NO WAY

band T-shirt
YES or NO WAY

bell bottoms
YES or NO WAY

hand-me-downs
YES or NO WAY

plaid
YES or NO WAY

yoga pants
YES or NO WAY

tank top
YES or NO WAY

overalls
YES or NO WAY

garden hat
YES or NO WAY

crocheted shirt
YES or NO WAY

Mirror, Mirror On My Wall

How I look in **ONE** word:

My **favorite perfume** is:
- ○ sweet
- ○ musky
- ○ fruity
- ○ flowery

My **favorite** jewelry:

My **favorite** color to wear:

My **favorite** kind of exercise:

My **favorite** piece of clothing:

My_____ is/are gorgeous.

feature or body part

The outfit that looks fantastic on me:

The latest **clothing trend** is:

I **take care** of myself by:

1.

2.

3.

4.

5.

My style is:
- classic
- funky
- goth
- tomboy
- dressy
- conservative
- rocker
- girlie
- preppy
- bohemian
- unique
- homemade

circle one

healthy food
or
junk food

I **RELAX** by:

My dream Closet

Cut out magazine photos of your favorite shoes, accessories, bags, dresses, and coats and put them in your closet.

Secret
Crushes...

shhh!

→ My first crush was on:

I would **never** be interested in someone who:

Most **important things** I've learned about having a crush:

Funniest pick-up line:

The best way to breakup:

_____

_____

_____

_____

_____

_____

_____

Someone's
heart
I broke:

The best way to get over a breakup:

_____

_____

_____

_____

_____

_____

Someone who
broke my
heart:

The Perfect Crush Machine

Put in your choices for the perfect crush.

Rate importance on a scale of 1 to 5, 5 being most important.

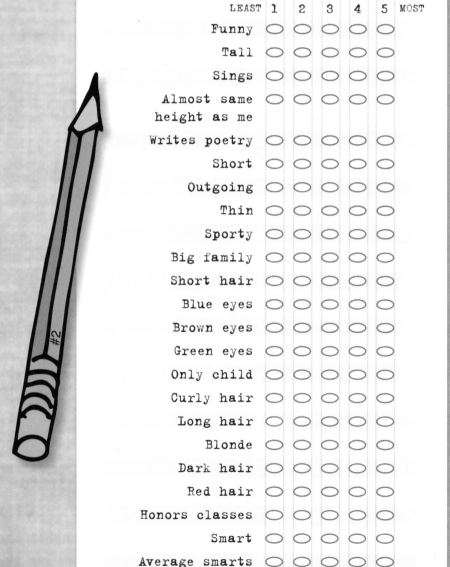

	LEAST 1	2	3	4	5 MOST
Funny	◯	◯	◯	◯	◯
Tall	◯	◯	◯	◯	◯
Sings	◯	◯	◯	◯	◯
Almost same height as me	◯	◯	◯	◯	◯
Writes poetry	◯	◯	◯	◯	◯
Short	◯	◯	◯	◯	◯
Outgoing	◯	◯	◯	◯	◯
Thin	◯	◯	◯	◯	◯
Sporty	◯	◯	◯	◯	◯
Big family	◯	◯	◯	◯	◯
Short hair	◯	◯	◯	◯	◯
Blue eyes	◯	◯	◯	◯	◯
Brown eyes	◯	◯	◯	◯	◯
Green eyes	◯	◯	◯	◯	◯
Only child	◯	◯	◯	◯	◯
Curly hair	◯	◯	◯	◯	◯
Long hair	◯	◯	◯	◯	◯
Blonde	◯	◯	◯	◯	◯
Dark hair	◯	◯	◯	◯	◯
Red hair	◯	◯	◯	◯	◯
Honors classes	◯	◯	◯	◯	◯
Smart	◯	◯	◯	◯	◯
Average smarts	◯	◯	◯	◯	◯

	LEAST 1	2	3	4	5 MOST
Musician	◯	◯	◯	◯	◯
Artist	◯	◯	◯	◯	◯
Vegetarian	◯	◯	◯	◯	◯
Cooks	◯	◯	◯	◯	◯
Class clown	◯	◯	◯	◯	◯
Honest	◯	◯	◯	◯	◯
Bookworm	◯	◯	◯	◯	◯
Freckles	◯	◯	◯	◯	◯
Good listener	◯	◯	◯	◯	◯
Confident	◯	◯	◯	◯	◯
Talkative	◯	◯	◯	◯	◯
Kind	◯	◯	◯	◯	◯
Straight A's	◯	◯	◯	◯	◯
Loyal	◯	◯	◯	◯	◯
Quiet	◯	◯	◯	◯	◯
Shy	◯	◯	◯	◯	◯
Similar interests	◯	◯	◯	◯	◯
Well-groomed	◯	◯	◯	◯	◯
Ambitious	◯	◯	◯	◯	◯
Nice smile	◯	◯	◯	◯	◯
Sensitive	◯	◯	◯	◯	◯
Adventurous	◯	◯	◯	◯	◯
Cute	◯	◯	◯	◯	◯
Glasses	◯	◯	◯	◯	◯
Well-dressed	◯	◯	◯	◯	◯
Prefers cats	◯	◯	◯	◯	◯
Likes dogs	◯	◯	◯	◯	◯
Prefers inside	◯	◯	◯	◯	◯
Prefers outside	◯	◯	◯	◯	◯

M.A.S.H. It UP Game

Are you ready to find out about your future life?

CRUSHES

NUMBERS

PLACES

HOUSE

Mansion
Apartment
Shack
House

Let's M.A.S.H. it up!

❶ In the blank spaces, write the names of four crushes, your favorite numbers, and places you'd like to live.

❷ Now, close your eyes and begin making dots on this page. After a short time or when your friend tells you to...stop! Count how many dots are on the page. This is your dot number.

❸ Starting on the first crush's name, count down through the entire list of answers until you reach your dot number. Whatever answer you're on, cross it off the list.

❹ Start counting again on the next answer. Skip over any crossed-off answers.

❺ Keep counting and crossing off until you only have one answer left in each category. Circle that answer.

❻ Write down your results below.

Results:

Who you're going to marry:

How many kids you'll have:

The place you'll live:

The house you'll live in:

My CRUSH CAPSULE

Glue an envelope here.

Place the name of your crush, the date, and any important details about your crush inside.

STaRRING ME

Everyone has special talents.
What makes you a shining star?

My sporty talent is:

My unusual talent is:

My hidden talent is:

My creative talent is:

a TaLENT I wish I had:

I'm a star because:

The Secret Me

What the secret me would like to say to
the world, but is too shy to let out...

helloooooo...

Daydreams
and Doodles

write down your wildest daydreams
and doodle what you think they mean.

LET IT OUT!

These venting pages are for you to whine, complain, and vent all about your pet peeves and things that get under your skin.

UGH!

And then...

Say WHAT?????

Don't you feel a little better?

MY TRAVELS AND ADVENTURES

For summer break, I went:

For spring break, I went:

The city I want to visit most:

A foreign city
I'd like to visit:

Most exotic place
I've visited:

Favorite country and why:

My Favorite...

Beach:

Winter vacation:

Road trip:

I don't want to go to:

WALKABOUT

The best thing about being on vacation is:

The **coolest thing** I've ever seen on vacation:

On my next trip, I want to:

- Take a gondola ride
- Ride a horse in the mountains
- Zipline through the rainforest
- Climb Kilimanjaro
- Go on a safari
- Snorkel in the Caribbean
- Climb the Eiffel Tower
- Sleep on a houseboat
- Hike a volcano
- Ride a camel
- Take a ride in a helicopter
- Explore a cave
- Learn to scuba dive
- Go snowboarding/skiing
- Swim with dolphins
- Ride the world's fastest roller coaster
- Shop on Rodeo Drive
- Go to Antarctica
- Visit the Galápagos Islands

A trip that my friend and I went on was:

World's Greatest Vacation...EVER!

Tell about the best vacation you've ever had.

WOULD YOU RATHER?

Circle the "THIS" or "THAT" you like best.

BLOND or BRUNETTE

GRAPES or CHERRIES

WATERBED or BUNK BED

DOGS or CATS

APPLE PIE or PUMPKIN PIE

NACHOS or POTATO CHIPS

CASTLE or COTTAGE

ALIEN or ROBOT

FRANKENSTEIN or DRACULA

RAINBOW or SHOOTING STAR

RICH or FAMOUS

ROCK CLIMBING or BUNGEE JUMPING

COTTON CANDY
or
CANDY APPLE

PENCIL or PEN

CAKE or ICE CREAM

HALF EMPTY
or
HALF FULL

PIE IN THE FACE
or
SLIP ON A BANANA PEEL

UNIQUE or NORMAL

RAIN or SNOW

TEXT or CALL

FAST or SLOW

INSIDE or OUTSIDE

CHICKEN or EGG

PIZZA or HAMBURGER

SCIENCE or CREATIVITY

FUNNY MOVIE or SCARY MOVIE

ZOO or AQUARIUM

DRIVE or FLY

SPELLING BEE
or
SCIENCE FAIR

GOLD or SILVER

ARM WRESTLING
or
THUMB WRESTLING

ROLLER COASTER
or
FERRIS WHEEL

JEANS or SKIRT

GROSS or SCARY

MASHED
POTATOES
or
STUFFING

GREEN HAIR or PURPLE HAIR

MEAT or VEGGIES

TORTOISE or HARE

CREAMY or CRUNCHY

ELEVATOR or ESCALATOR

WEST COAST or EAST COAST

HUNGRY or THIRSTY

MUSTARD or KETCHUP

PAST
or
PRESENT

STAYING UP LATE
or
GETTING UP EARLY

HEADS or TAILS

DEEP or SHALLOW

STILTS or UNICYCLE

BRAINS or BEAUTY

SQUARE or CIRCLE

MOVIE STAR or ROCK STAR

LEMONADE or HOT CHOCOLATE

BASEMENT or ATTIC

SUV or SPORTS CAR

✔ Been there,
✔ Done That!

Check off ALL that apply to you.

- ○ jumped into a pile of leaves
- ○ seen snow
- ○ driven a go-cart
- ○ broken a bone
- ○ come home after curfew
- ○ given a speech
- ○ had my name in the newspaper
- ○ won an award
- ○ danced in the rain
- ○ been to a concert
- ○ eaten rattlesnake
- ○ been on a reality TV show
- ○ drank coffee
- ○ traveled alone
- ○ had a surprise party thrown for me
- ○ baked a cake
- ○ had stitches
- ○ had a pie in the face
- ○ threw a pie in the face
- ○ entered a spelling bee
- ○ been in a sports league

- ◯ ridden an elephant
- ◯ had detention
- ◯ written a story
- ◯ written a song
- ◯ been scared of something under the bed
- ◯ saved someone
- ◯ swam with sharks
- ◯ been to the circus
- ◯ been skiing
- ◯ traveled out of the country
- ◯ ridden a horse
- ◯ been in a wedding
- ◯ gotten an A
- ◯ seen the movie *Sound of Music*
- ◯ done a front flip
- ◯ been on a roller coaster
- ◯ been scuba diving
- ◯ built a snowman
- ◯ told a lie
- ◯ caught a lizard
- ◯ been on a Jet Ski
- ◯ climbed a mountain
- ◯ read a book with more than 200 pages
- ◯ held a butterfly
- ◯ received flowers

In a Jam...

Describe the most difficult situation
that you've ever been in.

....

....

....

....

....

....

....

....

....

....

....

....

....

....

....

....

....

....

How'd you deal?

Truth or... Truth

Circle T or F for the following statements.
But you have to TELL THE TRUTH!

T or F I would slide down a steep water slide.

T or F I believe in déjà vu.

T or F I have sung in front of an audience.

T or F If I found money, I would turn it in.

T or F I enjoy sports.

T or F I have thought about my wedding.

T or F I have touched a dolphin.

T or F I have been to another country.

T or F I have baked a cake for someone.

T or F You can't change people.

T or F I believe in aliens.

T or F Ghosts are real.

T or F I ate mud pies as a child.

T or F I play with dolls.

T or F I believe that everything happens
        for a reason.

T or F   I can whistle.

T or F   I enjoy gossip.

T or F   I have lied to a friend.

T or F   I have never cheated on a test.

T or F   I want to have kids.

T or F   I am religious.

T or F   I have lied to my parents.

T or F   I eat my vegetables.

T or F   I do not eat meat.

T or F   I like sushi.

T or F   I have a crush on someone at school.

T or F   I like clowns.

T or F   I cry at sad movies.

T or F   I am grateful for what I have.

T or F   I am honest.

T or F   I am afraid of the dark.

T or F   I have had a job.

T or F   I have entered a beauty contest.

Oops! Did I do that?

What I said when I lied to my parental units:

How I really feel about lying:

A goal I never reached:

My worst habit:

A time when I was selfish:

TOP SECRET
Confessions

Write a secret confession that no one knows about on a small piece of paper.

Every time you have a secret you can add it to the envelope.

Fold up the small pieces of paper and put the secrets into an envelope and tape that to this page.

That's so **SCARY**

My biggest fear:

An irrational fear:

A fear I have about the future:

A dream that made me wake up in a cold sweat:

My **BIGGEST FEAR** when I was a kid:

Biggest **NATURAL DISASTER** fear:

My greatest fear for **THE WORLD** is:

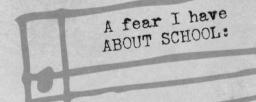

A fear I have **OVERCOME:**

A fear I have ABOUT SCHOOL:

FEAR-O-METER

Fill in the little thermometer on how scary these things are to you.

I can handle it	kinda scary	totally freaks me out

bees

not being liked

blood

the dark

thunder and lightning

small spaces

world news

roller coasters

speaking in class

needles

being laughed at

flying

spiders

roaches

water coasters

clowns

loud noises

hurricanes

ghosts

mice or rats

Guess Who's Coming to Your Party?

You're Invited!

Who:

Why:

If you could invite any three people (dead or alive) to your party, who would you want to be there and why?

You're Invited!

Who:

Why:

oh my, really?

You're Invited!

Who:

Why:

Ooooo, may I join you?

WISHING MACHINE

At night, I WISH:

I wish I could meet:

During school, I WISH:

When I'm at the mall, I WISH:

If I were on a magical island,
I'd wish for:

When I wish upon a star,
I wish for:

If I found a genie, I would wish for:

1

2

3

LaLa Land

If I could go back in time,
I would go to:

A piece of art I wish I created:

If I had a gazillion dollars,
I would:

If I could see the future,
I would want:

A singer I wish would sing to me:

In MY DREAMS,
I AM:
- a model
- an actor
- a doctor
- a singer
- a musician
- a pro athlete
- an artist
- a scientist
- CEO of my own company
- a world leader

if i could fly, I would go to:

Thanks-filled

What are you grateful for?

Doodle, scribble, or cut and paste images for the things that you're grateful for in your life.

How's Your Mood Quiz

1. If right now, you get a wrong number on your cell phone, you would

A. Shout "wrong number" and disconnect.

B. Mischievously continue the conversation, not revealing that the caller has the wrong number.

C. Politely say "You have the wrong number."

2. If you are surfing the Net for something important, and a fly starts buzzing around your ear, you

A. Squash that fly with your math book.

B. Catch it under a cup.

C. Shoo it away.

3. A friend sneaks up behind you in class and scares you. You would

A. Yell at her for scaring you.

B. Return the favor in the next class.

C. Laugh and say "Hi."

4. A friend was supposed to meet you at the mall, but didn't show up. She calls to apologize, you

A. Shout at her for not coming.

B. Ask her the reason. You'll get your revenge another time.

C. Believe her excuse and plan to meet another day.

5. Till now, your day has been

A. Bad.

B. The usual.

C. Very good.

6. Your plans for the evening have completely fallen apart, you

A. Throw your cell phone across the room.

B. Get upset but make other plans.

C. Relax and do something else just as fun.

7. Your BFF calls you with news. Your first thought is

A. Now what happened?

B. I hope it's good news.

C. I can't wait to hear your news.

ANSWERS: A's   B's   C's

Mostly A's. You are definitely in a bad mood. It might be best for you to stay away from people until your mood changes. You might try doing your favorite activity, going for a walk, or taking a hot bath to calm your frazzled nerves.

Mostly B's. Being a little mischievous is your mood of the day. It's okay to be a prankster once in a while, but be careful your mood doesn't turn into being mean.

Mostly C's. You are one happy girl! This day couldn't get any better for you, but it just might with this mood.

Wiki-me

If there were a **Wikipedia page** all about me,
here's what I'd like it to say.

My Awesome Year

I began this year:

I'm most proud about:

This year was better than last:
Yes   No Way
(Circle One)

My most **memorable moment** this year was:

My most **difficult task** this year was:

Things I learned about me this year:

I **felt inspired** this year when:

Coolest place I went this year:

I would like a **do-over on:**

Tell Why.

One thing that made my year fantastic:

The **biggest challenge** I had this year was:

My HOPES and DREAMS

Next year, I Want to feel:

The secret of my future happiness is:

I want to graduate college. **Yes** or **No**

I want to get married. **Yes** or **No**

I want to have kids. **Yes** or **No**

Being alone...a lot! **Yes** or **No**

One person I really Want to meet next year:

MY DREAM JOB WOULD BE:

A tradition I'd like to continue:

One thing I really want to accomplish next year:

In 5 years, I picture myself:

WHY I LOVE BEING ME. . .

THESE ARE A FEW OF

My Favorite THINGS

Book:

Writer:

Food:

Movie:

Vegetable:

Sport:

TV Show:

Way to Relax:

Vacation:

Fruit:

Restaurant:

Actor:

Athlete:

Flavor of Ice Cream:

Gadget:

Season:

Animal:

Holiday:

Store:

Singer:

Smell:

Song:

Color:

Board Game:

Quote:

Number:

Write a note to your future self.
Be sure to read it next year!

Hello, Future Me...